MOONQUAKE

Roy Bentley

HIPPO BOOKS
Scholastic Book Services
London

Scholastic Book Services Inc.,
10 Earlham Street, London, WC2H 9LN, England

Scholastic Book Services Inc.,
730 Broadway, New York N.Y. 10003, U.S.A.

Scholastic Tab Publications Ltd.,
3 Newkirk Road, Richmond Hill, Ontario L4C 3G5, Canada

All rights reserved
Printed in Spain by Mateu Cromo, Madrid

Ashton Scholastic Pty Ltd., PO Box 579,
Gosford, New South Wales, Australia

Ashton Scholastic Ltd.,
165 Marua Road, Panmure, Auckland, New Zealand

First published 1983 by André Deutsch Ltd.

Published in paperback by Scholastic Book Services Inc. 1984
Copyright © Anne and Roy Bentley 1983

Swinging silently and low over the moon's jagged
mountains a small white space-ship sped through the black
night of space. Suddenly its rocket motors burst into flame,
their mighty power slowing its headlong flight; exactly on
course for touchdown.
On the distant horizon lay the destination of scout-ship 317.
Picked out in the bright lunar sunrise were the vast
workings and strange buildings of Mining Base 5.

At the scout-ship's controls sat four space cadets, already qualified space pilots, calmly bringing their rocket in for a perfect landing.

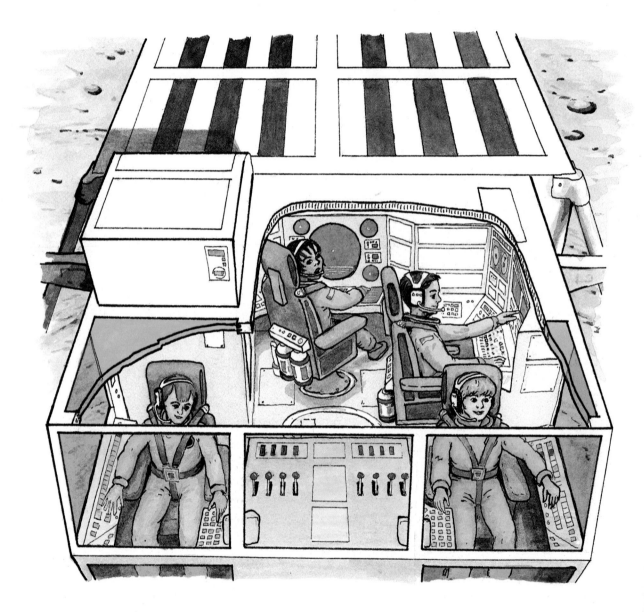

On arrival Tycho, Cassi, Ross and Gemma would start the next lesson in their training as "Spacers", members of the Space Rescue Service, the solar systems most highly trained astronauts able to cope with any emergency, anywhere.

"Height one hundred metres and hovering," reported Cassi at the radar screens. "Check," agreed Ross, their pilot, "Auto-pilot off, commence manual landing. Throttle engines back to point nine five."

Slowly the scout-ship sank towards the landing pad. "Ten metres, five, two, one, DOWN!" called Cassi. "Cut engines, vent pumps, all flight systems off!" commanded Tycho at the computer control board. Instantly the ship changed from a blazing flying rocket, to a silent machine standing firmly on the ground.

"317 landed," Gemma the co-pilot reported to Base Control, "rocket safe to approach."

Slowly two moon lorries drove towards them from the base, bringing maintenance crews to take over the ship from the cadets.

A moon bus parked under the front, and clipped into the entry hatch. Climbing down, the four cadets found the Mining Base Commander in its small cabin.

"Welcome to Mining 5," he greeted them, "I thought I'd come and tell you about your mission myself. It's an important job, and instead of flying a space-ship you'll be learning what it's like to work down here on the moon."

"We've a big operation here," he went on, "with millions of tonnes of high grade ore still to dig out. But one day it'll all be gone, and we need to know years in advance where to dig next."

"This is your mission," he said, handing them a thick bundle of maps and instructions. "The satellite surveys on a nearby valley look really promising. You're to be prospectors, and check if they're right!"

The moon bus stopped alongside a large mobile drilling rig. Already in their space-suits, the cadets climbed out and walked towards the huge vehicle that was to be their home for the next ten days.
It had been built from a large lunar excavator, but with two bits added. In the middle, between the driving cabin and the atomic power plant, the living rooms for their trip had been fixed. At the back a giant drilling frame reached up towards the stars.

The frame's powerful motors would drill a long tube deep into the moon, and bring out samples of rock. The team's job was to collect these samples, hundreds of them, for the scientists back at the mining base laboratories.

"Let's get started," called Tycho, "This is going to be good!"

So Gemma keyed in the motors and pulled away. Following the route map she turned towards the distant mountains and their valley.

On the long drive out they were able to take turns at driving, learning about the rig, eating and sleeping. They studied their instructions and maps and planned the mission. "Galloping Galaxies!" exclaimed Tycho, "This mission looks like hard work!"

Cassi looked thoughtful, "I imagined a prospector was one old man with two tired mules, not four astronauts, hundreds of tonnes of machinery and thousands of atomic horse power."

"That's progress," sighed Ross.

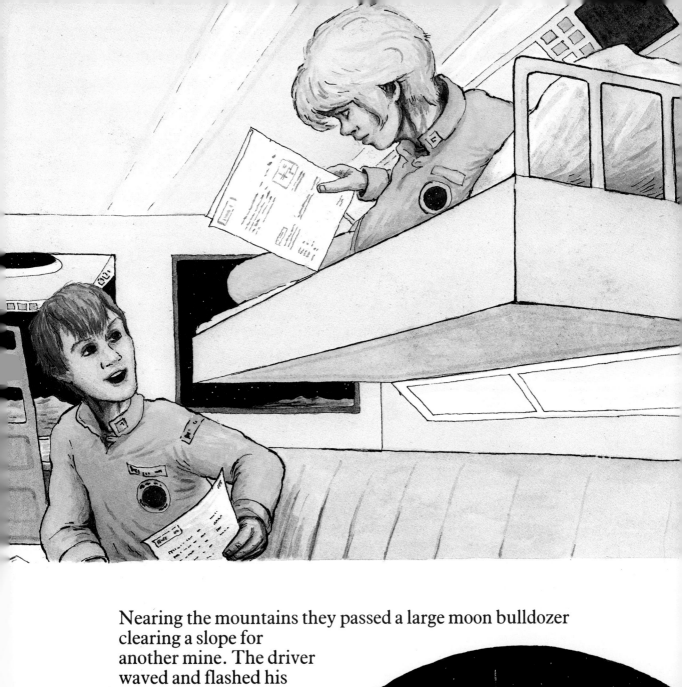

Nearing the mountains they passed a large moon bulldozer clearing a slope for another mine. The driver waved and flashed his lights without stopping. He didn't seem to have any time to spare, the cadets thought unhappily.

Four hours later they crowded into the driving cabin as Cassi turned into the valley. The sight was fantastic. Two great walls of rock reared up on each side of a narrow entrance, like the huge ruined towers of an ancient castle gate. Beyond, the cliffs opened out into a wide valley encircled by tall mountain peaks.

There were no footprints or tyre tracks anywhere, only the jumbled pitted surface formed millions of years before. Entirely alone, they stood where no man had been before!

Once in the valley the mission really began. Wearing their space-suits the cadets put up a small flashing light, marking its position carefully on the map. As they drove cautiously across the rough barren ground they stopped every kilometre to set up another, until a long line of these miniature lighthouses stretched down the valley's length. At the foot of the mountains they started drilling. Row after row of bore holes, each one exactly a hundred metres apart, but each one with different problems. Sometimes the ground sloped up, sometimes down, often rocks and boulders had to be cleared out of the way by the digging blade before the drilling could begin.

It was hard, difficult work. Cassi was inside, driving the huge lumbering machine with pin-point accuracy. Ross, Gemma and Tycho stayed ouside, directing her, checking their position against the flashing lights, loading the drill tubes into the frame, and collecting the samples.

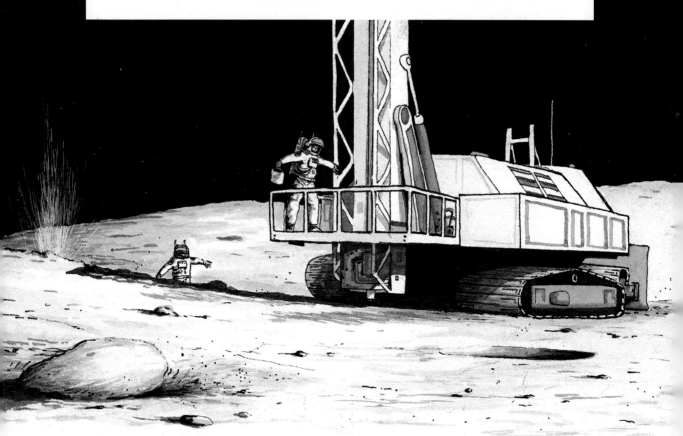

By the third day they were half way back up the valley and Tycho was removing a rock sample from the raised drill.

"O.K.," he reported, "Bore hole H/107, Sample 6 in bag 4/1 ... WHAT IN SPACE WAS THAT?"
"What's up?" Ross asked.
"*There*, there it is again," Tycho shouted and this time they all felt it. The valley floor was moving, trembling, shuddering.
"It's ... it's a ..."

"MOONQUAKE, MOONQUAKE, MINING 5
CALLING ALL RESCUE UNITS. DISASTER,
DISASTER, HELP."
The urgent call rang from their headphones on a special
channel kept for emergencies only.
"Space cadets 317 to Space Rescue Control," called Cassi.
"Can we help?"
"Negative 317," Spacers Control replied, "You're two days
drive away. Our rockets will reach Mining 5 in half an
hour." A moment later Control came through again,
"We've lost contact with a bulldozer just outside your
valley, all our craft are busy, can you investigate?"

"We're on our way!" they shouted.

Leaping and bouncing over the rough stony surface they raced the rig up the valley. Cassi pushed the mighty atomic engine to its limit, driving at an almost impossible, crazy speed. Spacers Control had heard nothing from the moondozer since the quake. It couldn't be found by radar or seen through the satellite telescopes. The huge machine and its driver had just disappeared.

The valley entrance was blocked. The quake had smashed the great rock walls, and a huge bank of rubble lay right across their path. Without hesitation Cassi drove straight at it, the tracks slipped and spun, the rig slewed from side to side but kept on going.

Up and up, slower and slower it went, then for one terrible moment it stopped, balanced on the top, its spinning tracks fighting for a grip. They were stranded, not sliding back but unable to go on.

Slowly, very very slowly the rig tipped forwards, the tracks caught. They were through!

In a cloud of dust Cassi braked the speeding rig to a shuddering halt; they had reached the spot where four days earlier they had spotted the moondozer and its driver. Everything had changed, the gently rolling slope was now a jumbled mess of rock falls, land slides, boulders and huge gaping cracks. "Jupiter!" gasped Gemma, "If it's as bad as this here what must it be like at Mining Base 5."

"Don't even think about it," urged Ross, "our job is to find that digger quickly. I bet it's down one of these cracks."

It took ten hours of difficult dangerous searching, but they found it. Wedged upside down in a seemingly bottomless crevasse it lay bashed, battered, but not broken apart. "The driver could still be alive in there," called Cassi "We'll have to drag him out!"

Tied on by one slim safety line Tycho crawled backwards into that black bottomless pit. Inching his way down the loose broken rocks with infinite care, he stepped at last onto the dozer's left track. "Hang on tight, Ross," he whispered into his helmet radio, hardly daring to breathe. "This thing's stuck on a ledge and it could fall off at any moment."

"Check. I've got you," Ross replied calmly. Tycho edged along the dozer's underframe "Right, I'm at the back now, send down the towing chain."

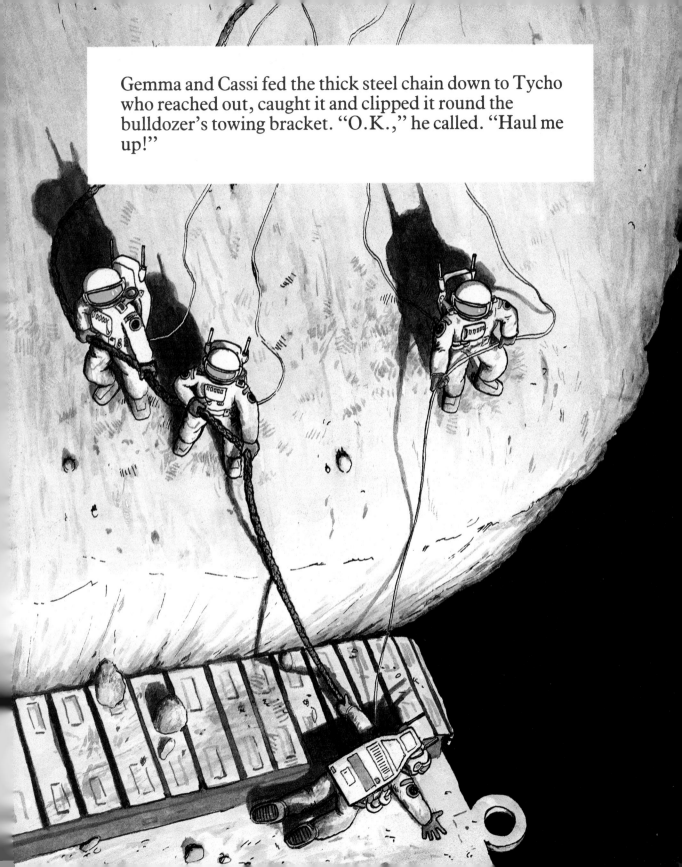

Gemma and Cassi fed the thick steel chain down to Tycho who reached out, caught it and clipped it round the bulldozer's towing bracket. "O.K.," he called. "Haul me up!"

"Pull!" called Gemma, and Cassi set the rig into reverse on half power. The chain straightened, both tracks gripped and slowly the straining machine clawed its way back. "The end's lifting!" called Ross, "It's coming out!"

But is wasn't. The rear end lifted less than a metre, then
stuck. Cassi turned up to full power, but that was too much
– the tracks spun, grinding the surface into dust and
throwing stones high into the star studded sky.
"It's no good," reported Tycho, "it's jammed!"

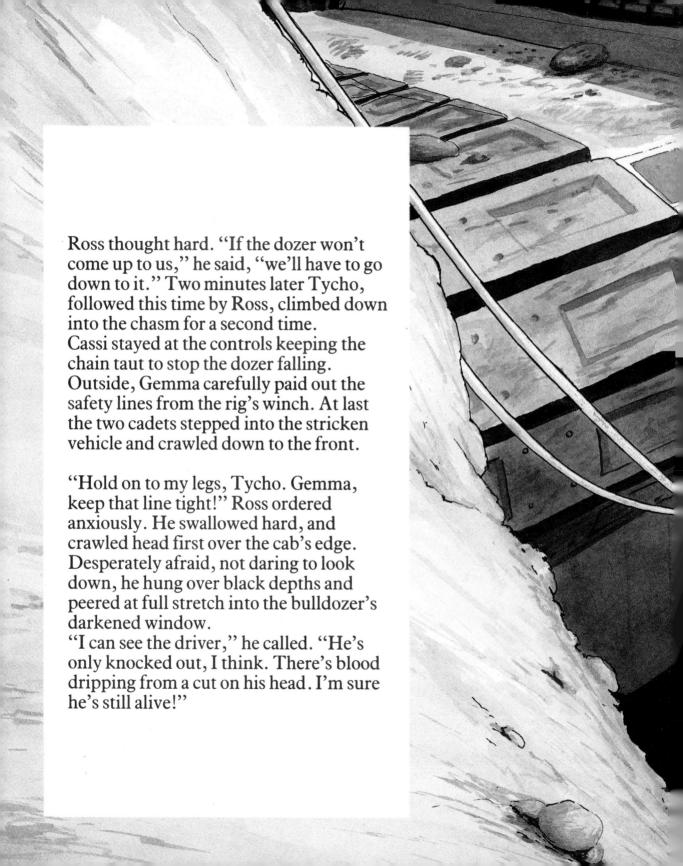

Ross thought hard. "If the dozer won't come up to us," he said, "we'll have to go down to it." Two minutes later Tycho, followed this time by Ross, climbed down into the chasm for a second time. Cassi stayed at the controls keeping the chain taut to stop the dozer falling. Outside, Gemma carefully paid out the safety lines from the rig's winch. At last the two cadets stepped into the stricken vehicle and crawled down to the front.

"Hold on to my legs, Tycho. Gemma, keep that line tight!" Ross ordered anxiously. He swallowed hard, and crawled head first over the cab's edge. Desperately afraid, not daring to look down, he hung over black depths and peered at full stretch into the bulldozer's darkened window.
"I can see the driver," he called. "He's only knocked out, I think. There's blood dripping from a cut on his head. I'm sure he's still alive!"

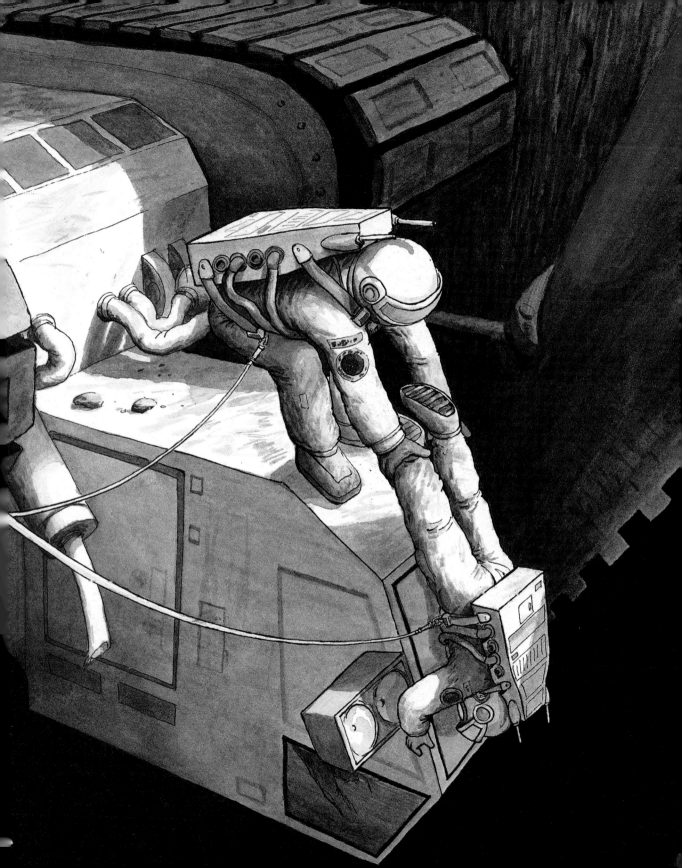

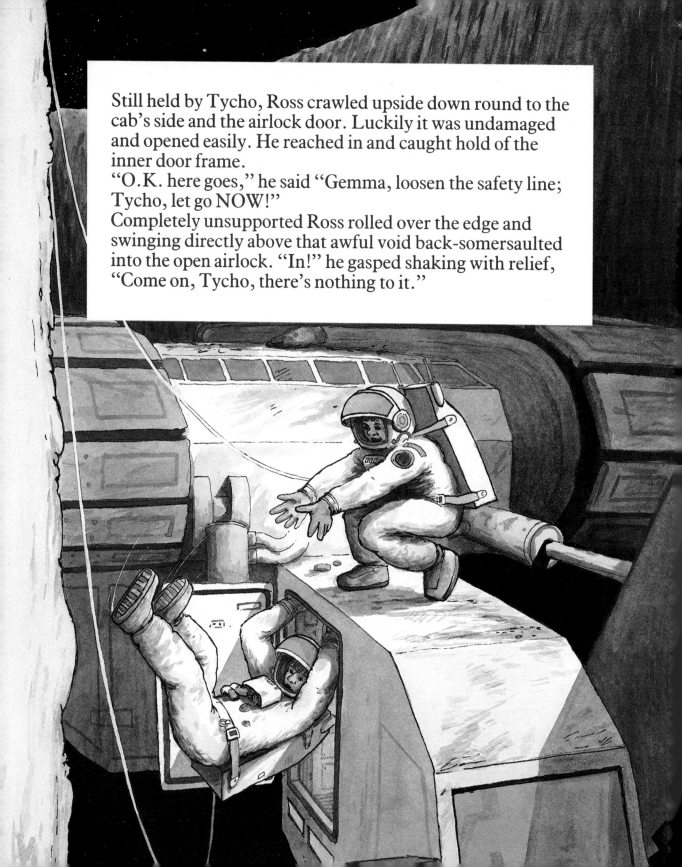

Still held by Tycho, Ross crawled upside down round to the cab's side and the airlock door. Luckily it was undamaged and opened easily. He reached in and caught hold of the inner door frame.

"O.K. here goes," he said "Gemma, loosen the safety line; Tycho, let go NOW!"

Completely unsupported Ross rolled over the edge and swinging directly above that awful void back-somersaulted into the open airlock. "In!" he gasped shaking with relief, "Come on, Tycho, there's nothing to it."

The inside of the upturned cab was a jumbled mess of
smashed and broken equipment. The injured driver hung
upside down in his safety harness, blood dripping down
onto the ceiling below. Tycho and Ross cut the unconscious
man down, eased him carefully into his space - suit and
checked that it had no tears. "We're on our way back," they
reported to Cassi and Gemma, "send down two more safety
lines."

Already exhausted by the downward climb, the two astronauts now had to bring back the driver's heavy, unconscious body.

Tycho hauled himself up onto the dozer's underside, ready to help. "O.K.," he said, "Start pulling up."

Slowly Cassi and Gemma winched in the driver's safety lines. Ross eased the limp body out of the airlock and over the rough, rocky wall below Tycho. Nobody spoke, as they all concentrated on their own part in this difficult, critical job – one tear in the driver's space suit would be fatal.

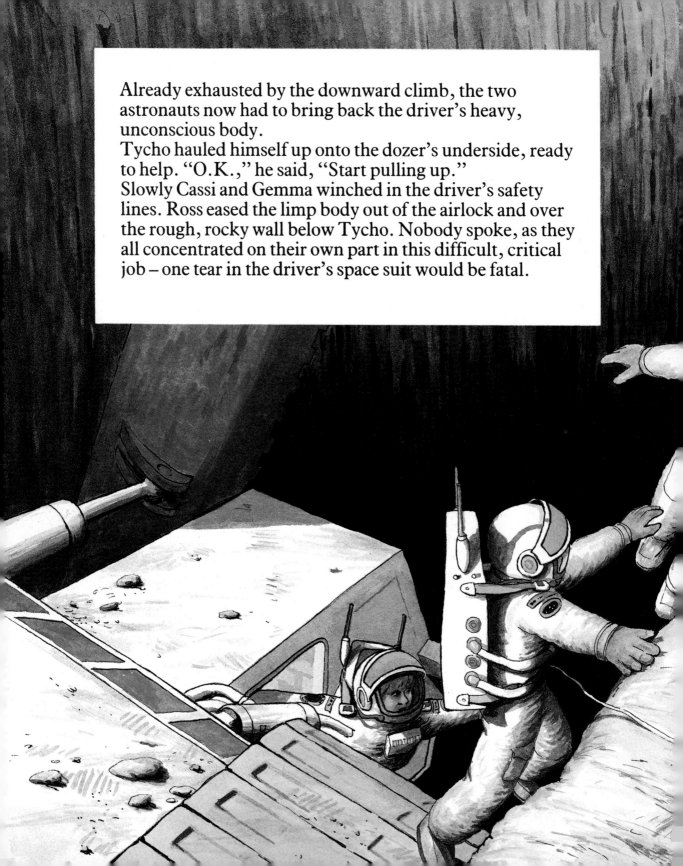

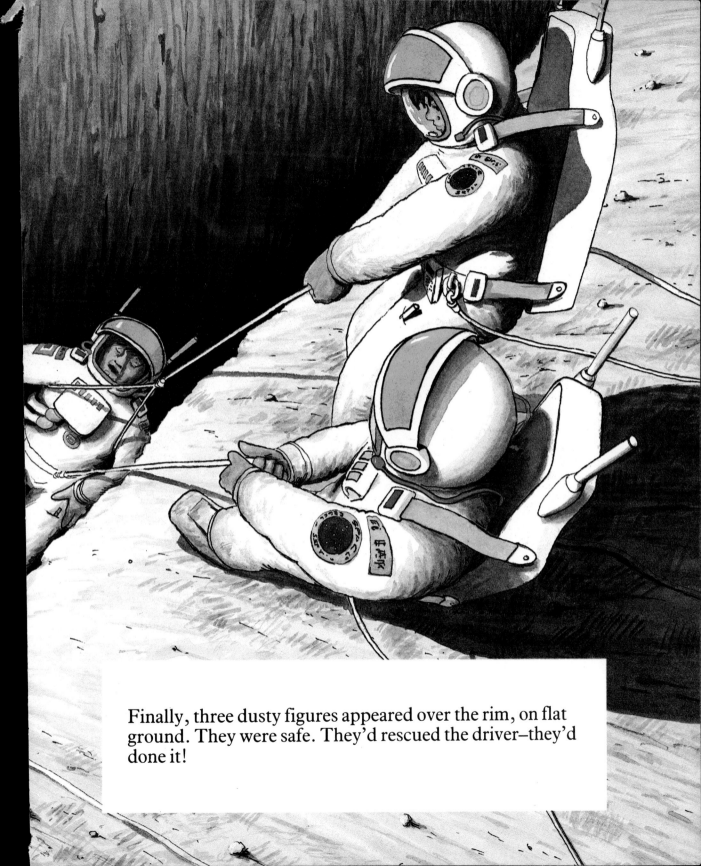

Finally, three dusty figures appeared over the rim, on flat ground. They were safe. They'd rescued the driver–they'd done it!

Four minutes later the cadets and the slowly recovering driver gazed upwards into the black sky. High above a Space Rescue Hospital Ship was firing its retro-rockets and coming into land.

"We're ordered back to base," Cassi told the others, "No more prospecting for us this year."
"Well that was one way of getting out of a lot of hard work, I suppose," joked Ross and even the driver joined in with their laughter.